# Circle the ladybug that has **0** spots.

# Circle the cupcake that has **0** stripes.

# Write the number

# 1

## Trace the number, then write it yourself.

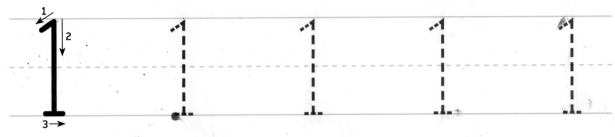

one

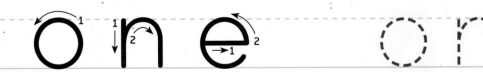

# Circle the flower that has **1** bee.

# Circle the king that has **1** jewel in his crown.

# Write the number

# 2

Trace the number, then write it yourself.

2  2  2  2  2

two

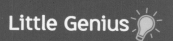

# Circle the bus that has **2** passengers.

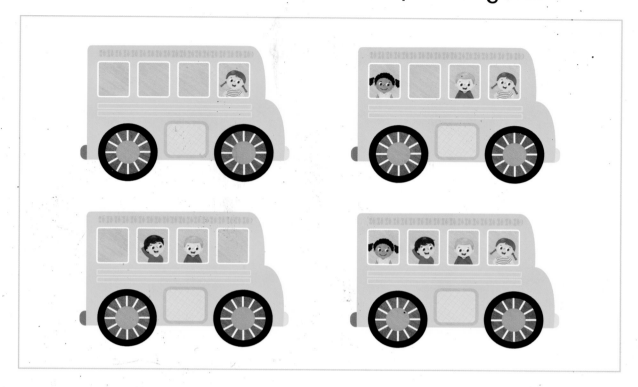

# Circle the scarecrow that has **2** birds.

# Write the number

## 3

Trace the number, then write it yourself.

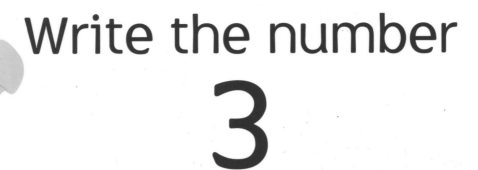

three

# Circle the pod that has **3** peas.

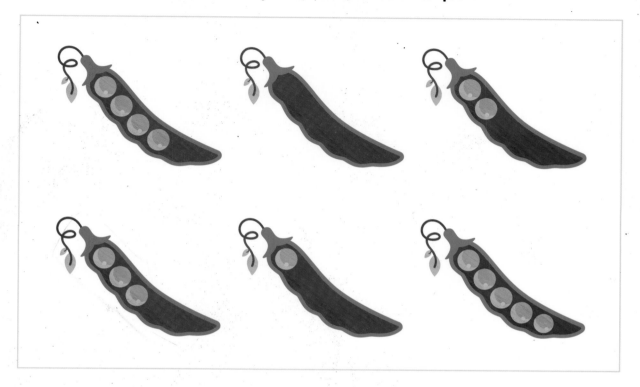

# Circle the clown that has **3** balloons.

# Write the number

# 4

Trace the number, then write it yourself.

# four

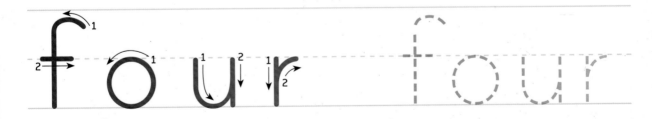

# Circle the tree with **4** apples.

# Circle the vase that has **4** flowers.

# Write the number

# 5

Trace the number, then write it yourself.

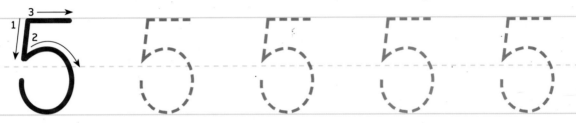

# five

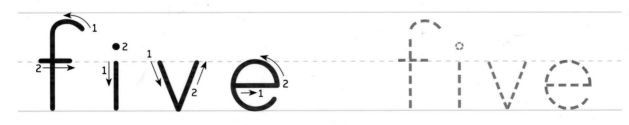

# Circle the carton that has **5** eggs.

# Circle the fishbowl that has **5** fish.

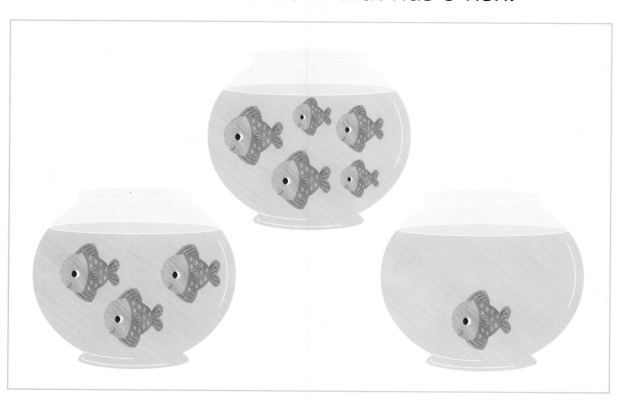

# Write the number
# 6

Trace the number, then write it yourself.

## six

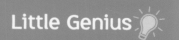

# Circle the cookie that has **6** chocolate chips.

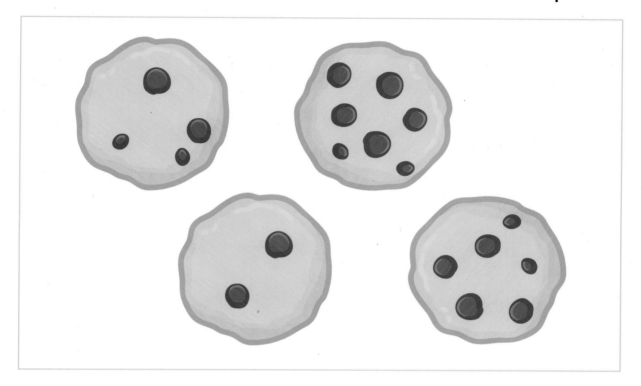

# Circle the flower that has **6** petals.

# Write the number
# 7

Trace the number, then write it yourself.

7 7 7 7 7

## seven

# Circle the birthday cake that has **7** candles.

# Circle the jar that has **7** pencils.

# Write the number

# 8

Trace the number, then write it yourself.

8 8 8 8 8

# eight

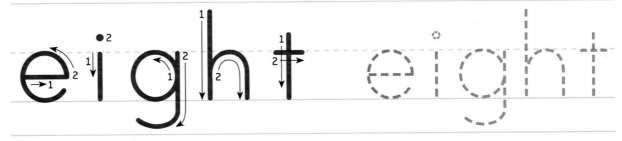

# Circle the octopus that has **8** legs.

# Circle the lamp that has **8** stars.

# Write the number

# 9

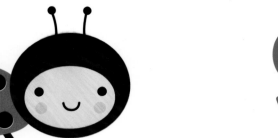

Trace the number, then write it yourself.

# nine

# Circle the cloud that has **9** raindrops.

# Circle the ice cream that has **9** sprinkles.

# Write the number
## 10

Trace the number, then write it yourself.

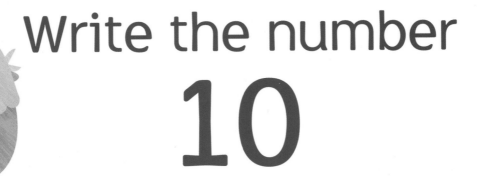

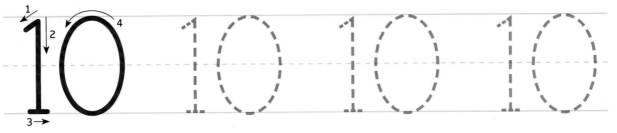

ten

# Circle the bunch that has **10** grapes.

# Circle the plate that has **10** strawberries.

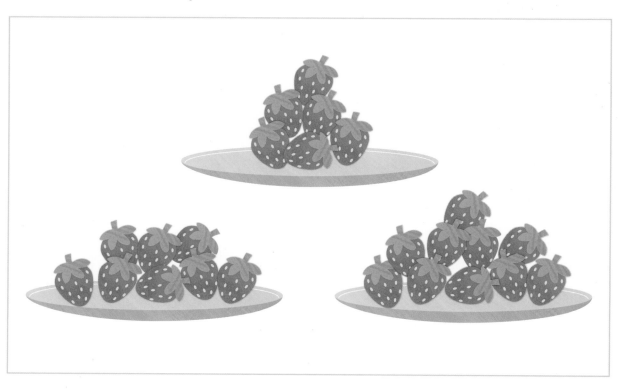

# Circle the race car

Circle the race car with the number **7** on the door.

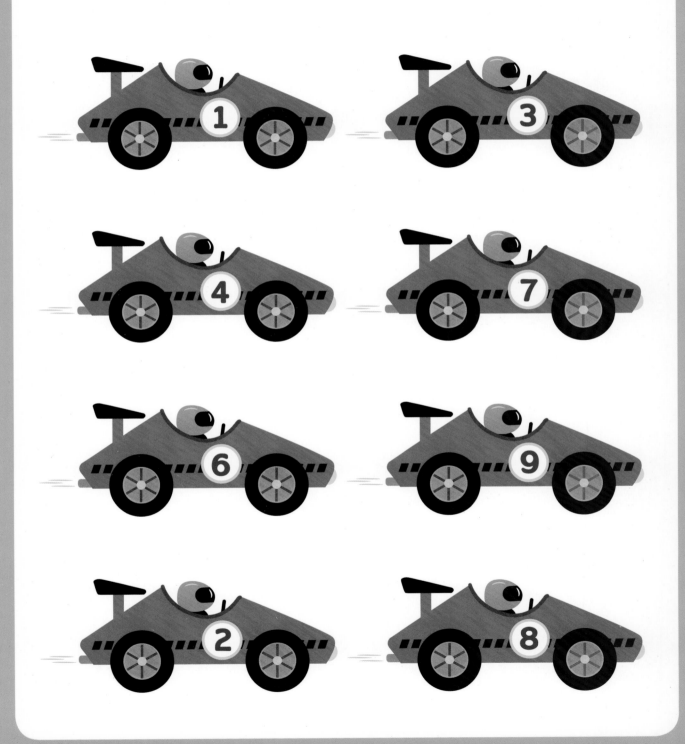

# Count the windows

How many windows can you see on the houses? Circle the right answer for each one.

1 2 3 4

1 2 3 4

# Circle the shoes

Circle all the shoes with **3** stripes on them.

# Complete the picture

Draw more buttons so there are
**6** buttons in each jar.

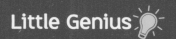

# Odd one out

## Circle the odd one out.

## Circle the odd one out.

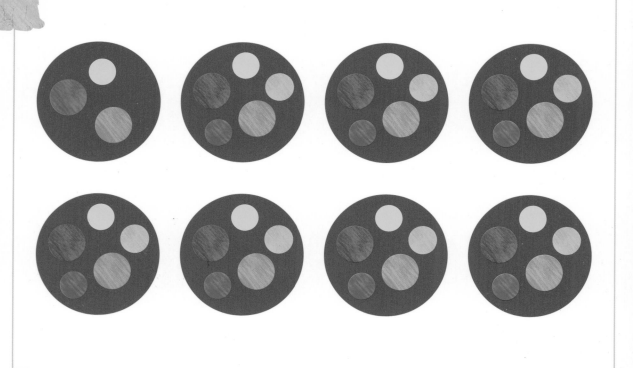

# Complete the picture

On each flower, draw the number of petals that is written in the middle.

# Which one has more?

In each section, circle which group has more.

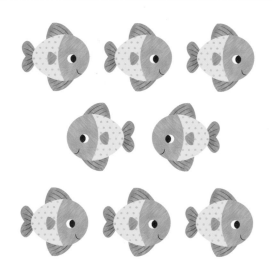

# Let's count!

Tick a box in the grid for each object you find.

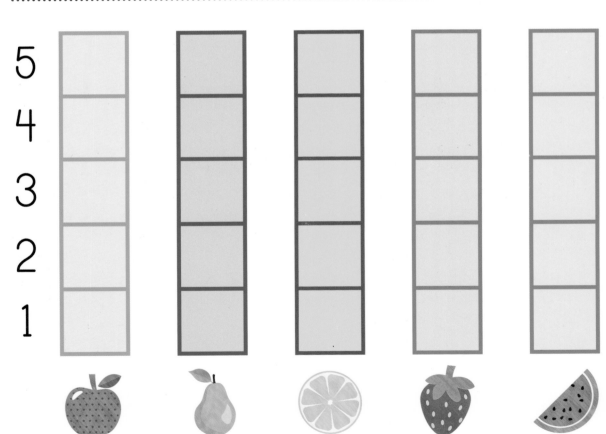

# Let's count!

Tick a box in the grid for each object you find.

5
4
3
2
1

# Write the number

# 11

Trace the number, then write it yourself.

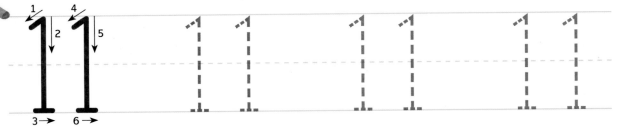

# eleven

# Trace around **11** of these balloons.

# Write the number
# 12

Trace the number, then write it yourself.

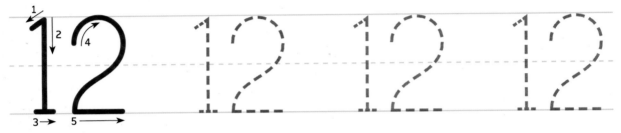

## twelve

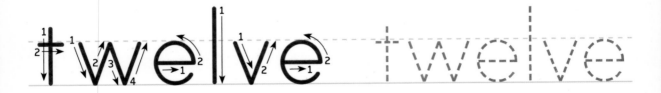

# Circle **12** leaves.

# Write the number

# 13

Trace the number, then write it yourself.

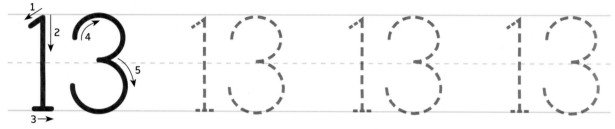

# thirteen

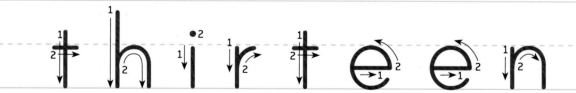

# Circle all the **13**s in the number scramble.

8    13    11    4

13    18    13    2

20    2    9    5

1    10    13    7

13    6    16    3

# Write the number

# 14

## Trace the number, then write it yourself.

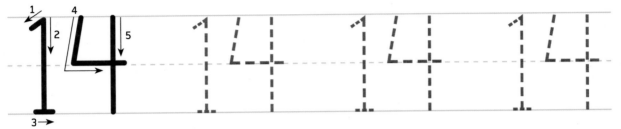

# fourteen

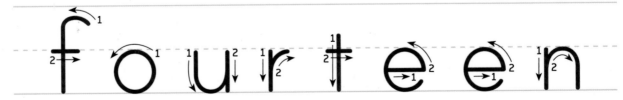

# Draw a line to connect every number **14** to help the bird get to its nest.

# Write the number

# 15

## Trace the number, then write it yourself.

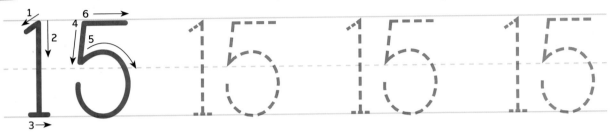

# fifteen

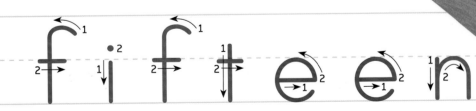

# Draw a line to match the number to the word.

 13

 11

 14

 10

 15

 12

twelve

ten

fifteen

fourteen

eleven

thirteen

# Write the number
# 16

Trace the number, then write it yourself.

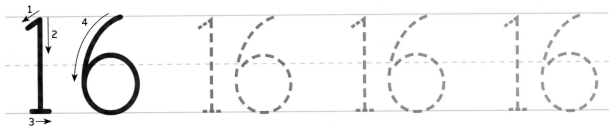

## sixteen

Look at the octopuses and answer
these questions.

How many
legs?

How many
spots?

# Write the number
# 17

## Trace the number, then write it yourself.

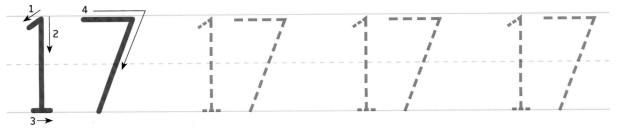

# seventeen

# Circle **17** hearts.

# Write the number
# 18

Trace the number, then write it yourself.

# eighteen

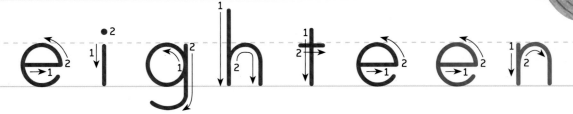

Circle all the **18**s in the number scramble.

11 1 15 12 18

13 18 13 2 18

20 4 9 5 2

7 18 16 10 3

18 19 2 6 13

14 18 6 16 3

# Write the number

# 19

Trace the number, then write it yourself.

# nineteen

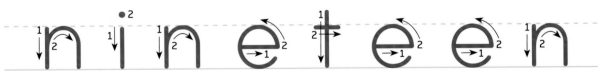

# Trace around **19** of these cupcakes.

# Write the number

# 20

Trace the number, then write it yourself.

# twenty

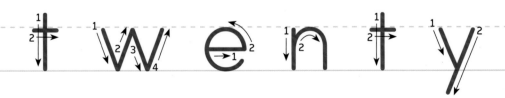

# Connect the dots from **0** to **20** to complete the picture.

# Counting to 20

Follow the numbers from **0** to **20**
to help the bird find its nest.

| 0 | 1 | 2 | 20 | 6 | 2 | 17 | 4 |
| 6 | 19 | 3 | 9 | 18 | 8 | 9 | 10 |
| 8 | 13 | 4 | 5 | 6 | 7 | 1 | 11 |
| 3 | 18 | 15 | 0 | 12 | 4 | 2 | 12 |
| 7 | 4 | 11 | 20 | 2 | 15 | 14 | 13 |
| 12 | 6 | 13 | 18 | 9 | 16 | 3 | 1 |
| 18 | 9 | 0 | 12 | 11 | 17 | 18 | 19 |
| 8 | 17 | 4 | 10 | 6 | 2 | 4 | 20 |

# How many?

How many balloons is the monkey holding?
Write the answer in the box.

# How many?

How many bees can you see? Write the answer in the box.

# Find the objects

Count the objects and write how many there are of each of them.

stars     rocket ships

astronauts [ ]    planets

# Count the socks

How many socks are hanging on the clothesline? Write your answer in the box.

# Complete the picture

Draw smiley faces on **12** of the circles.

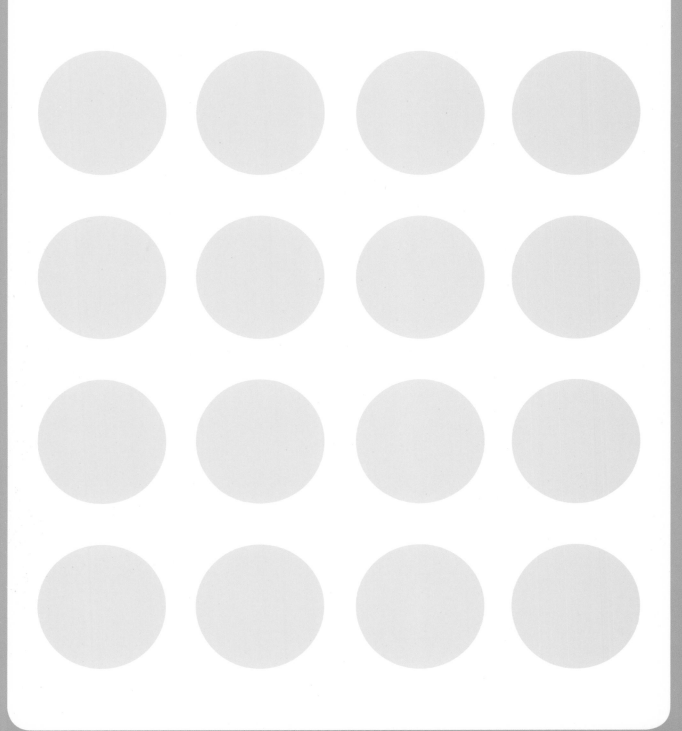

# How many legs?

Count the legs of all the animals,
and write the total number of legs in the box.

How many legs?

# Count the seeds

Count the seeds on each watermelon
and write the number in the box.

# Count the objects

Count the objects and then draw a line
to match them to the correct number.

14

12

16

13

# What comes before?

What number comes before? Write the missing numbers in the boxes.

| | | | |
|---|---|---|---|
| | 12 | 13 | 14 |
| | 5 | 6 | 7 |
| | 3 | 4 | 5 |
| | 8 | 9 | 10 |
| | 16 | 17 | 18 |

# What comes after?

Count forward to fill in the missing numbers in each row.

| 1 | 2 | 3 | |
| 5 | 6 | 7 | |
| 10 | 11 | 12 | |
| 13 | 14 | 15 | |
| 17 | 18 | 19 | |

# What comes in between?

What number comes in between?
Write the missing numbers in the boxes.

| 2 | | 4 | 5 |
|---|---|---|---|
| 6 | 7 | | 9 |
| 10 | | 12 | 13 |
| 13 | 14 | | 16 |
| 17 | | 19 | 20 |

# What's missing?

Write the missing numbers on the blank t-shirts.

# What's missing?

Write the missing numbers in the bubbles.

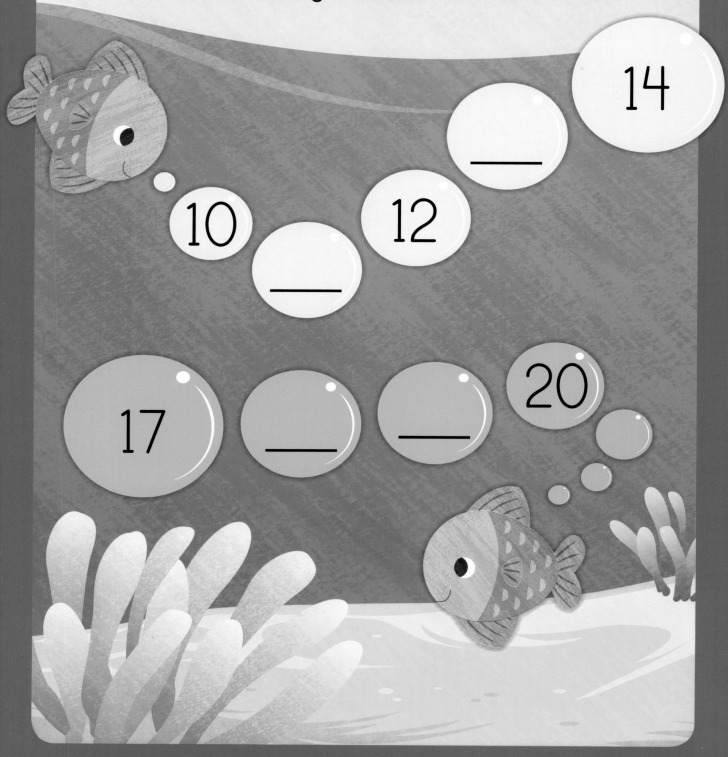

# What's missing?

The puzzle pieces count back from **10** to **0**.
Write the missing numbers.

# Find the yo-yo!

Draw a line from **20** to **1** to help the girl find the yo-yo.

| | 5 | 8 | 2 | 4 | 11 |
|---|---|---|---|---|---|
| 20 | 19 | 18 | 6 | 7 | 3 |
| 5 | 7 | 16 | 17 | 4 | 7 | 5 |
| 10 | 14 | 15 | 2 | 5 | 3 | 15 |
| 3 | 13 | 1 | 7 | 19 | 18 | 11 |
| 7 | 12 | 14 | 16 | 3 | 2 | 13 |
| 10 | 11 | 6 | 5 | 4 | 1 | |
| 9 | 8 | 7 | 12 | 15 | | |

# Number lines

Help the frog jump forward on the line to add the numbers. Write your answers in the boxes.

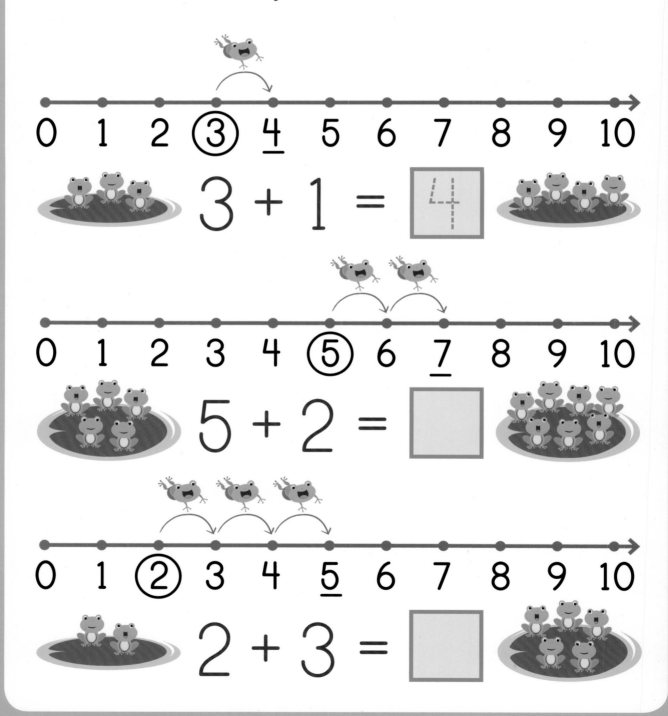

0  1  2  ③  4  5  6  7  8  9  10

3 + 1 = 4

0  1  2  3  4  ⑤  6  7  8  9  10

5 + 2 = 

0  1  ②  3  4  5  6  7  8  9  10

2 + 3 =

# Number lines

Help the frog jump forward on the line to add the numbers. Write your answers in the boxes.

0 1 2 3 4 5 6 7 8 9 10

$$4 + 1 = \boxed{\phantom{0}}$$

0 1 2 3 4 5 6 7 8 9 10

$$2 + 5 = \boxed{\phantom{0}}$$

0 1 2 3 4 5 6 7 8 9 10

$$6 + 3 = \boxed{\phantom{0}}$$

# Add the groups

Add the two groups, then write
the answer in the box.

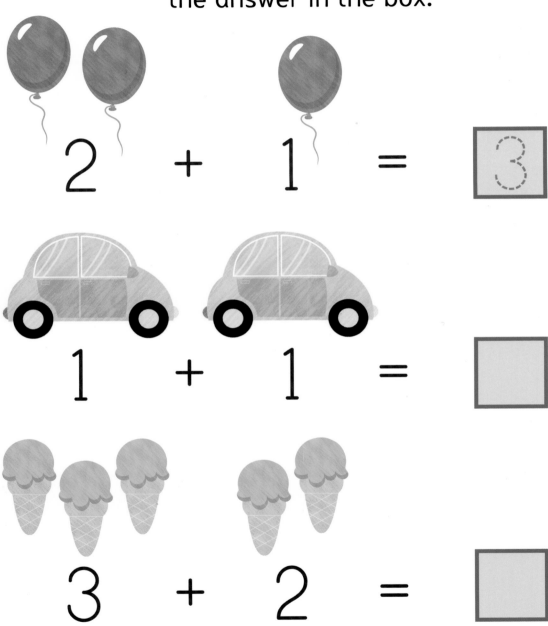

$2 + 1 = 3$

$1 + 1 = \square$

$3 + 2 = \square$

0 1 2 3 4 5 6 7 8 9 10

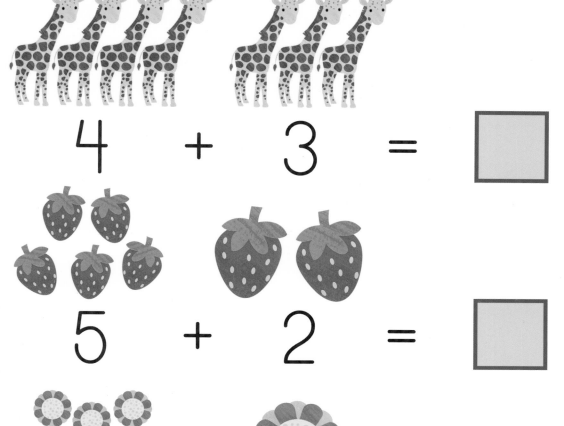

4 + 3 = ☐

5 + 2 = ☐

8 + 1 = ☐

6 + 3 = ☐

0   1   2   3   4   5   6   7   8   9   10

# Follow the path

Help the pirate get to the treasure.
Start at **0** and step along two spaces to add **2**.
Shade the square you land on. Then step two
more spaces to add another **2**. Shade that square
too. Keep going until you reach the treasure.

# Add 2

Look at the pirate's path to help you work out the answers to these sums.

$0 + 2 =$

$2 + 2 =$

$4 + 2 =$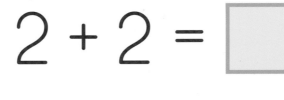

$6 + 2 =$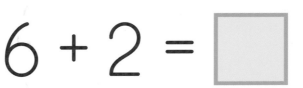

$8 + 2 =$

Little Genius

# Add the groups

Write how many objects are in each group. Then, add the two groups and write your answer in the box.

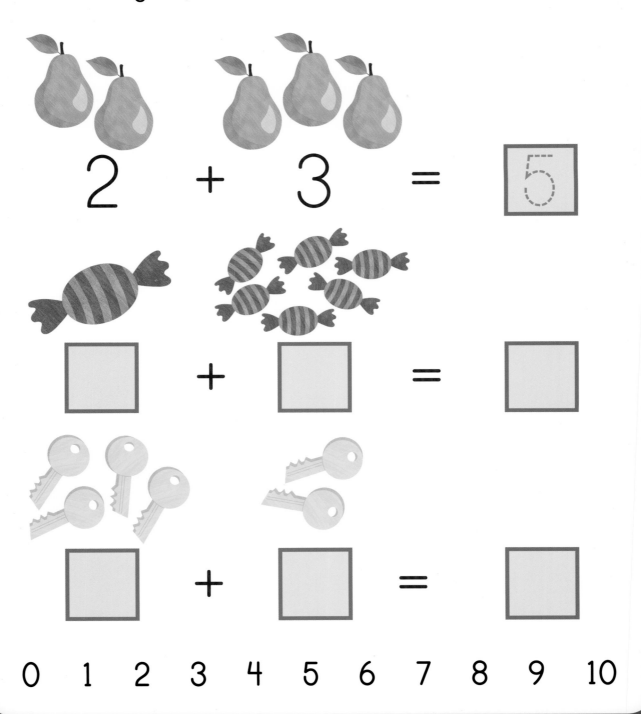

$$2 + 3 = 5$$

0   1   2   3   4   5   6   7   8   9   10

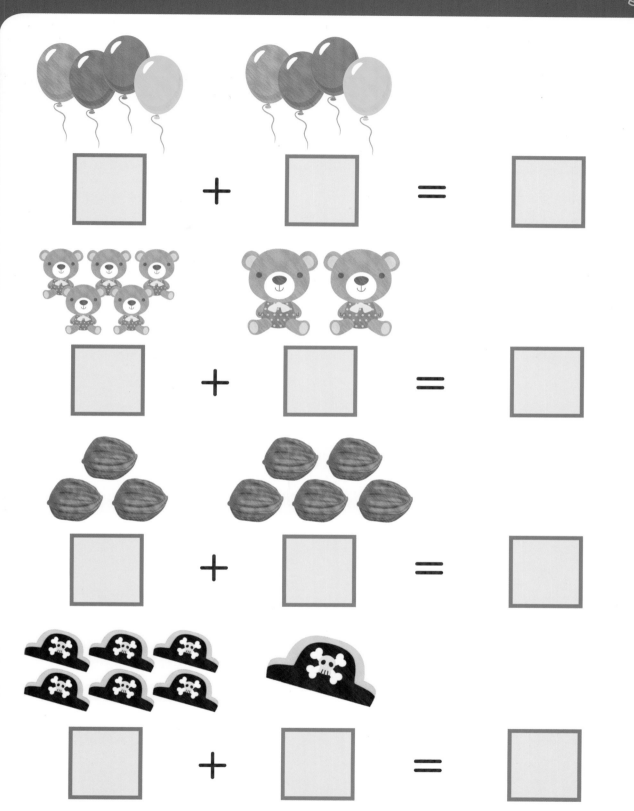

0 1 2 3 4 5 6 7 8 9 10

# Complete the picture

There are **3** flowers in the first vase. Draw **2** flowers in the second vase. How many flowers are there altogether? Write your answer in the box.

3    +    2    =

# Complete the picture

There is **1** person on the train. Draw **3** more people in the carriages. How many people are there altogether? Write your answer in the box.

1 + 3 =

# Find the sums

Circle the sums that equal **6**.

2 + 4

1 + 3

3 + 3

4 + 2

5 + 1

6 + 2

0  1  2  3  4  5  6  7  8  9  10

# Find the sums

Circle the sums that equal **8**.

1 + 7

7 + 3

2 + 4

4 + 4

3 + 5

6 + 2

0  1  2  3  4  5  6  7  8  9  10

# Count the dots

Count the dots on the dice and write the sum.
Add the numbers together and write the answer
in the box.

☐ + ☐ = ☐     ☐ + ☐ = ☐

☐ + ☐ = ☐     ☐ + ☐ = ☐

☐ + ☐ = ☐     ☐ + ☐ = ☐

# Match the dominoes

Draw a line to match the dominoes to the sums.
Then, write the answer in the box.

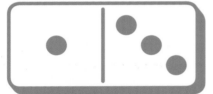

$$1 + 3 = \boxed{\phantom{0}}$$

$$6 + 1 = \boxed{\phantom{0}}$$

$$3 + 5 = \boxed{\phantom{0}}$$

$$4 + 6 = \boxed{\phantom{0}}$$

$$2 + 2 = \boxed{\phantom{0}}$$

$$4 + 4 = \boxed{\phantom{0}}$$

# Number lines

Help the frog jump backward on the line to subtract the numbers. Write your answers in the boxes.

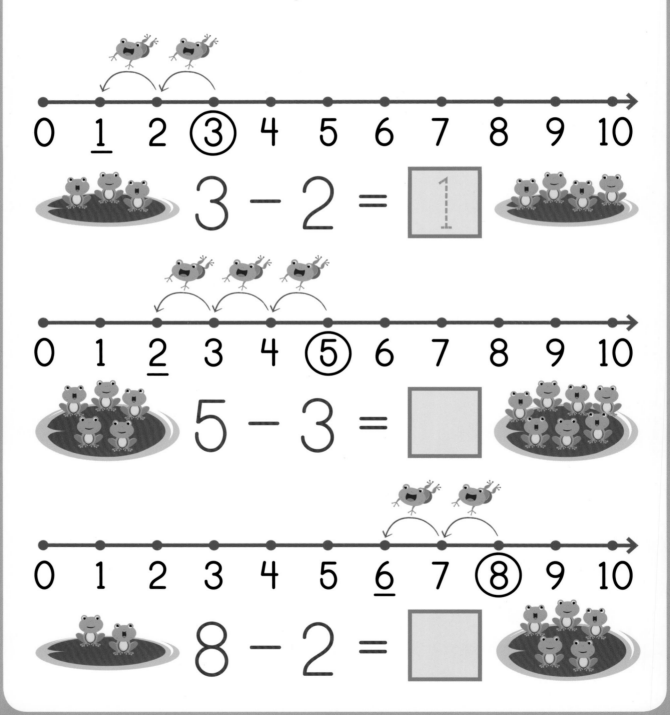

$3 - 2 = \boxed{1}$

$5 - 3 = \boxed{\phantom{0}}$

$8 - 2 = \boxed{\phantom{0}}$

# Number lines

Help the frog jump backward on the line to subtract the numbers. Write your answers in the boxes.

0   1   2   3   4   5   6   7   8   9   10

$$9 - 6 = \boxed{\phantom{0}}$$

0   1   2   3   4   5   6   7   8   9   10

$$7 - 4 = \boxed{\phantom{0}}$$

0   1   2   3   4   5   6   7   8   9   10

$$10 - 5 = \boxed{\phantom{0}}$$

# Subtraction

Subtract the second group from the first group.
Then, write your answers in the boxes.

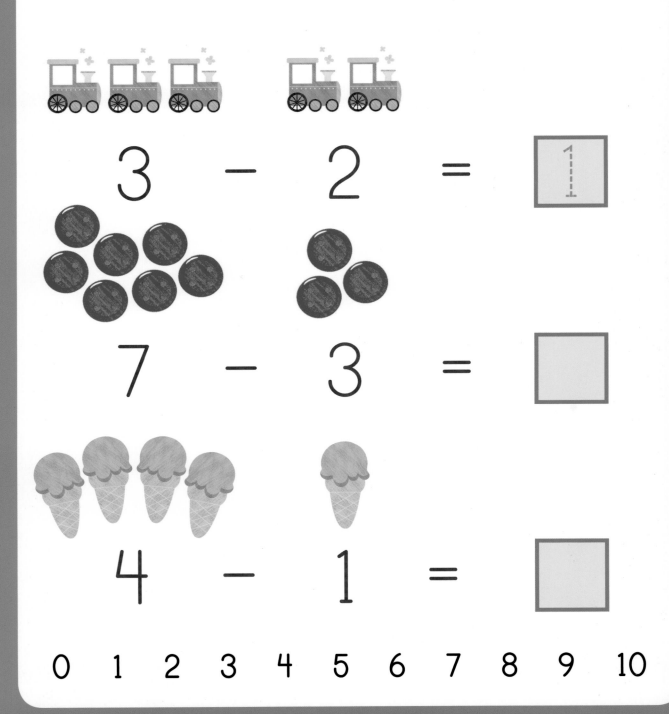

3 − 2 = 1

7 − 3 =

4 − 1 =

0  1  2  3  4  5  6  7  8  9  10

6 − 4 = [ ]

8 − 3 = [ ]

5 − 1 = [ ]

10 − 4 = [ ]

0   1   2   3   4   5   6   7   8   9   10

# Subtract the groups

Write how many objects are in each group.
Then, subtract the second group from the first
one and write your answer in the box.

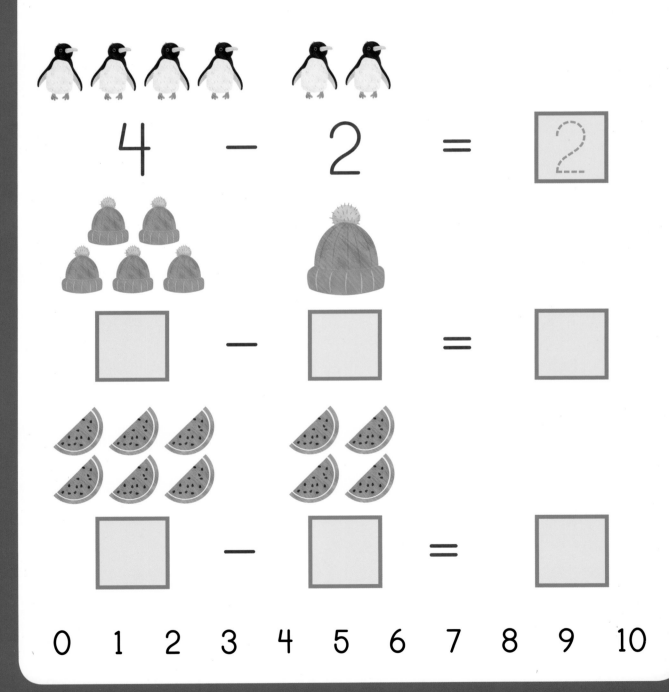

4 − 2 = 2

□ − □ = □

□ − □ = □

0  1  2  3  4  5  6  7  8  9  10

0   1   2   3   4   5   6   7   8   9   10

# Complete the sum

Fill in the missing numbers to complete the sums.

4   –    2   =   2

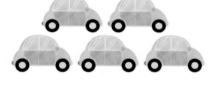

5   –   [ ]   =   4

3   –   [ ]   =   1

0   1   2   3   4   5   6   7   8   9   10

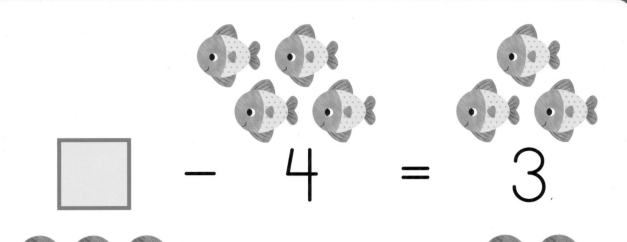

☐ − 4 = 3

6 − ☐ = 4

☐ − 3 = 2

9 − ☐ = 5

0   1   2   3   4   5   6   7   8   9   10

# Complete the picture

There are **9** sweets in the jar. You eat **5** of them. Cross them out. How many sweets are in the jar now? Write your answer in the box.

9   –   5   =   [ ]

# Complete the picture

There are **8** apples in the tree. You pick **3** of them. Cross them out. How many apples are there now? Write your answer in the box.

$$8 - 3 = \boxed{\phantom{0}}$$

# Find the sums

Circle the sums that equal **3**.

5 – 4

6 – 3

8 – 1

7 – 4

5 – 3

9 – 9

0  1  2  3  4  5  6  7  8  9  10